play BASS with... PAUL McCARTNEY

play BASS with... PAUL McCARTNEY

Wise Publications part of The Music Sales Group London / New York / Paris / Sydney / Copenhagen / Berlin / Madrid / Tokyo

Published by
Wise Publications
14-15 Berners Street, London W1T 3LJ, UK.

Exclusive Distributors:
Music Sales Limited
Distribution Centre, Newmarket Road, Bury St Edmunds, Suffolk IP33 3YB, UK.
Music Sales Pty Limited
120 Rothschild Avenue, Rosebery, NSW 2018, Australia.

Order No. AM985215
ISBN 978-1-84609-479-8
This book © Copyright 2007 Wise Publications, a division of Music Sales Limited.

Music arranged by Arthur Dick.
Music processed by Paul Ewers Music Design.
Compiled by Nick Crispin.
Edited by David Weston.
Printed in the EU.

CD recorded, mixed and mastered by Jonas Persson.
All guitars by Arthur Dick.
Bass by Paul Townsend.
Drums by Chris Baron.

Your Guarantee of Quality
As publishers, we strive to produce every book to the highest commercial standards.
The music has been freshly engraved and the book has been carefully
designed to minimise awkward page turns and to make playing from it a real pleasure.
Particular care has been given to specifying acid-free, neutral-sized paper made from
pulps which have not been elemental chlorine bleached.
This pulp is from farmed sustainable forests and was produced with special regard for the environment.
Throughout, the printing and binding have been planned to ensure a sturdy,
attractive publication which should give years of enjoyment.
If your copy fails to meet our high standards, please inform us and we will gladly replace it.

www.musicsales.com

play BASS with...
PAUL McCARTNEY

ANOTHER DAY

Words & Music by Paul McCartney & Linda McCartney

It's just a-noth-er day.____ 2. At the off-ice world her pa-pers grow, she

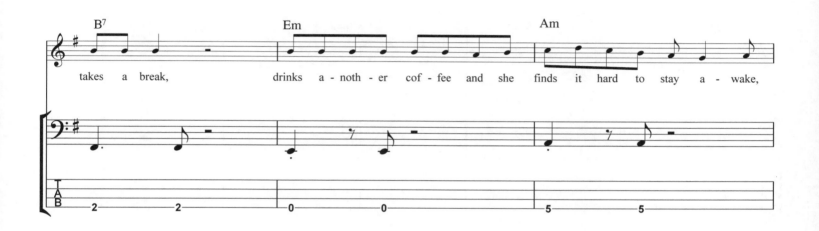

takes a break, drinks a-noth-er cof-fee and she finds it hard to stay a-wake,

it's just a-noth-er day.____ Do do do do do do, it's just a-noth-er day.

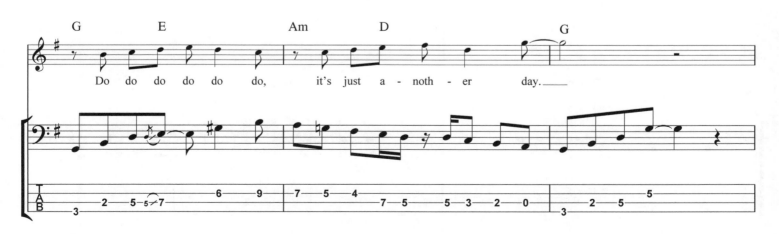

Do do do do do do, it's just a-noth-er day.____

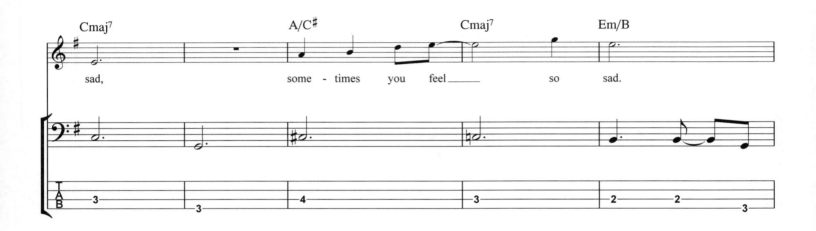

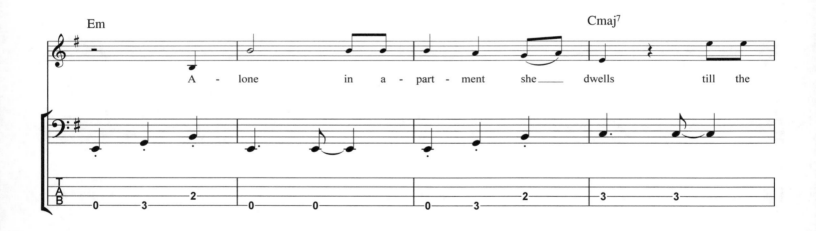

Ah, _____ stay. Don't stand her

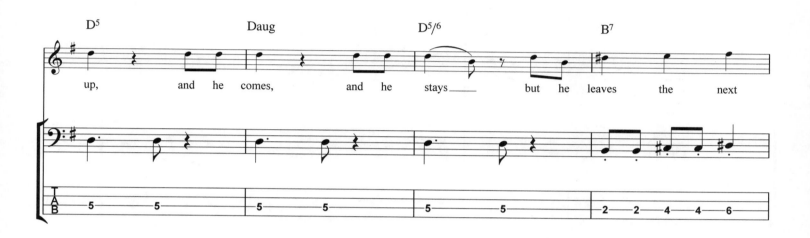

up, and he comes, and he stays _____ but he leaves the next

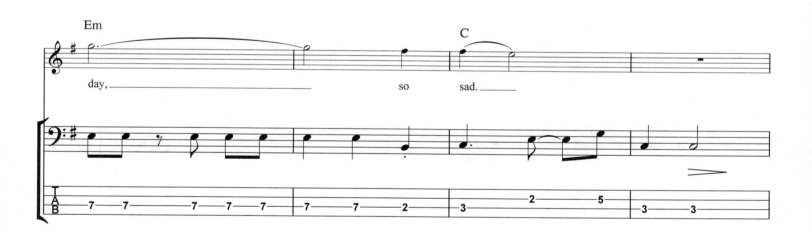

day, _____ so sad. _____

Some - times you feel _____ so sad. 3. As she

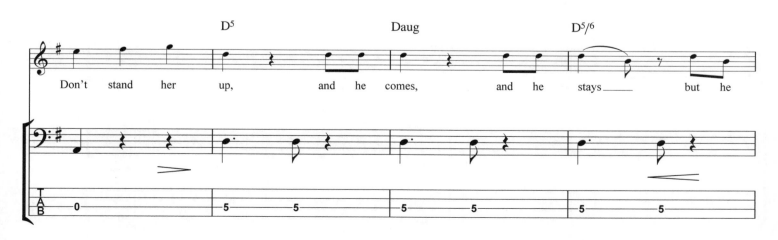

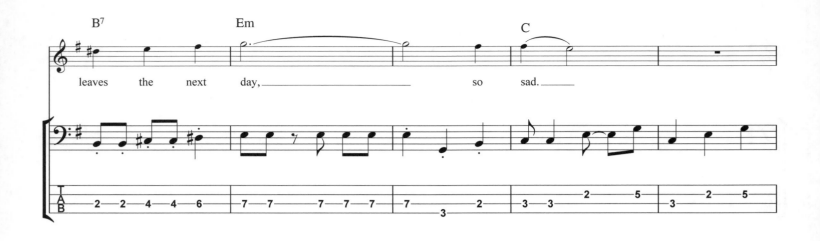

leaves the next day, _____ so sad. _____

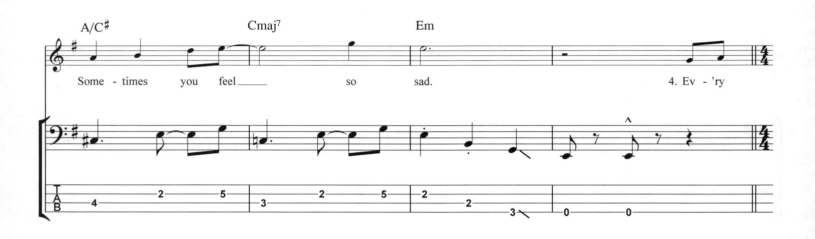

Some - times you feel _____ so sad. 4. Ev - 'ry

Verse

day she takes her morn - ing bath to wet her hair, wraps a towel a - round her as she's

head - ing for the bed - room chair, _____ it's just a - noth - er day. _____

ANYWAY

Words & Music by Paul McCartney

Intro

1 bar count in:

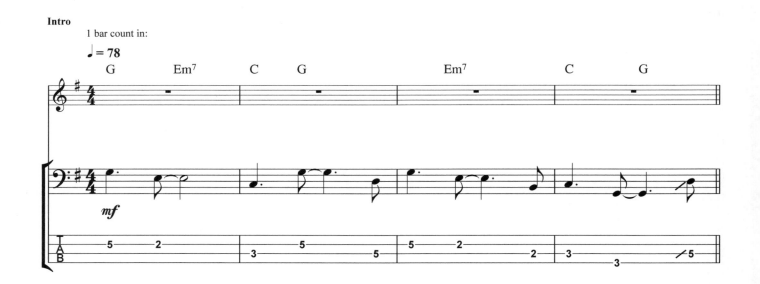

Verse

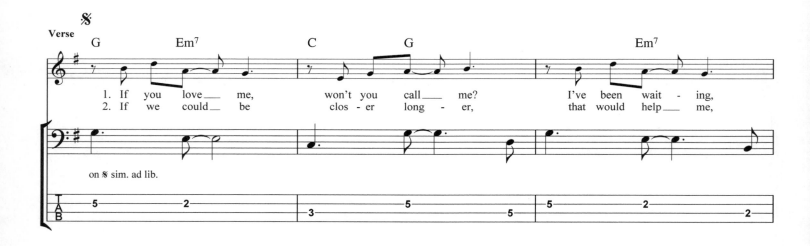

1. If you love___ me, won't you call___ me? I've been wait - ing,
2. If we could___ be clos - er long - er, that would help___ me,

on % sim. ad lib.

wait - ing too___ long.___ In my soul___ is con - stant yearn - ing;
help me so___ much.___ We can cure___ each oth - er's sor - row;

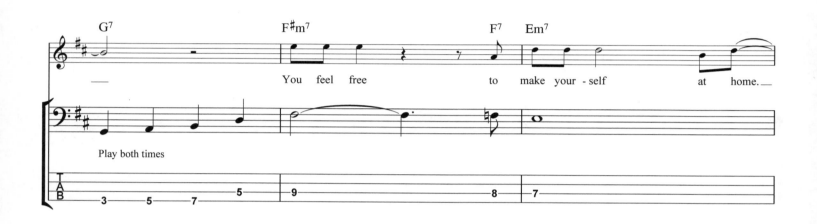

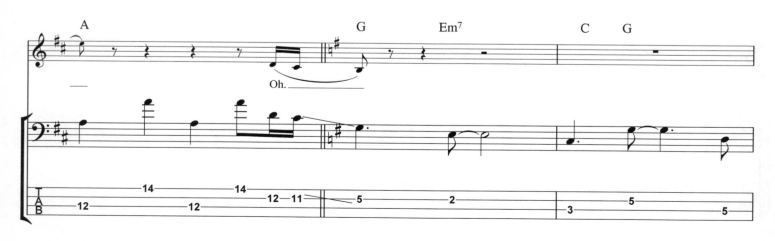

D.S. al Coda   ⊕ **Coda**

An - y - way,

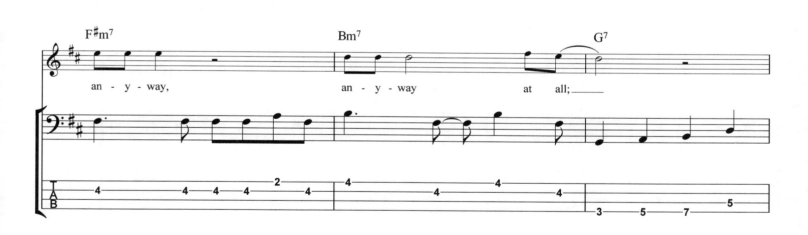

an - y - way,   an - y - way   at   all;

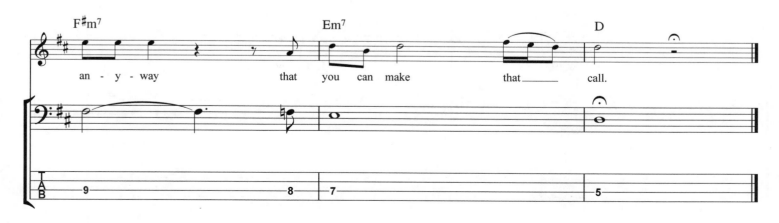

an - y - way   that   you   can   make   that   call.

BAND ON THE RUN
Words & Music by Paul McCartney & Linda McCartney

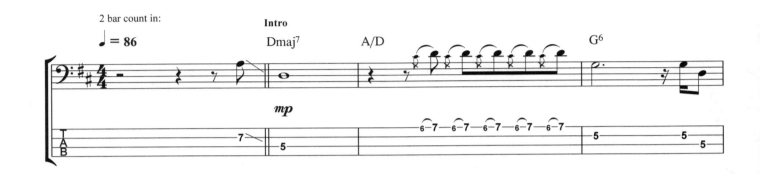

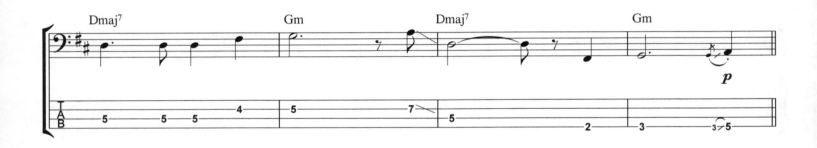

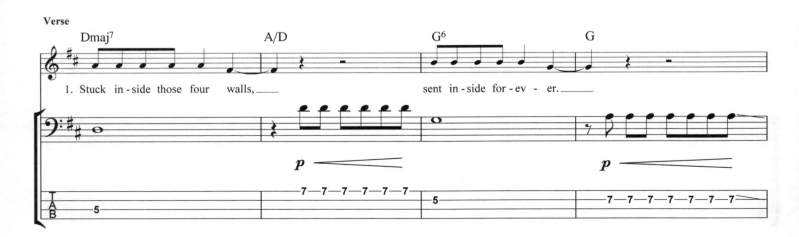

1. Stuck in-side those four walls, ___ sent in-side for-ev-er. ___

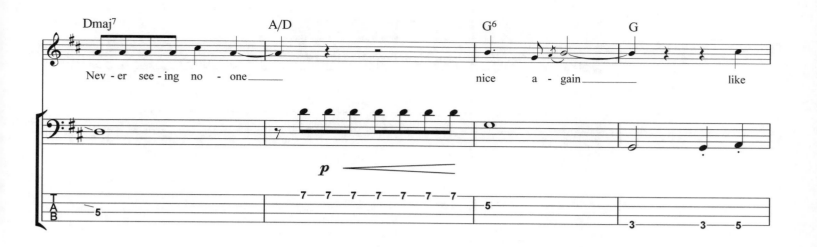

Nev - er see - ing no - one   nice a - gain   like

you.   Ma - ma,   you.   Ma - ma,

Bridge

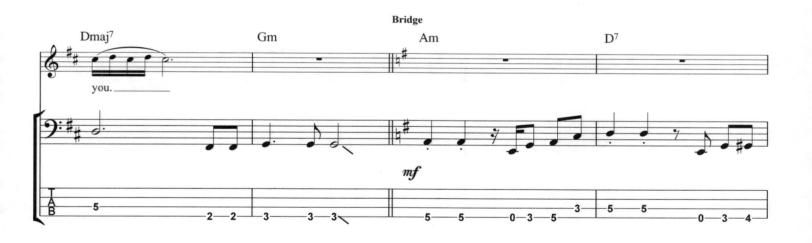

you.

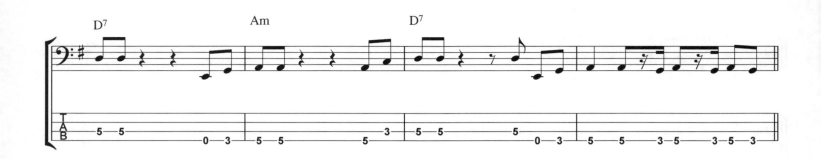

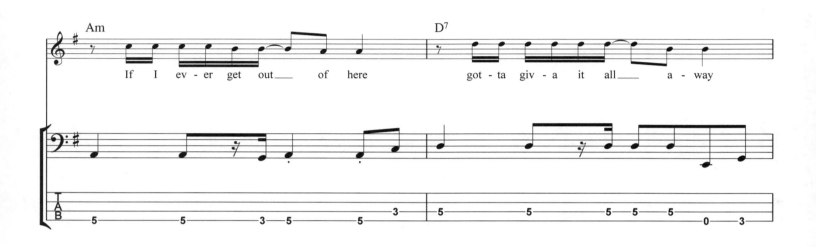

If I ev-er get out__ of here gott-a giv-a it all__ a - way

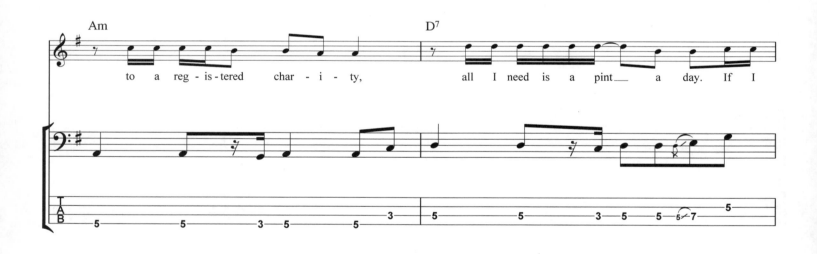

to a reg - is - tered char - i - ty, all I need is a pint__ a day. If I

ev - er get out__ of here. If we ev - er get out__ of here.__

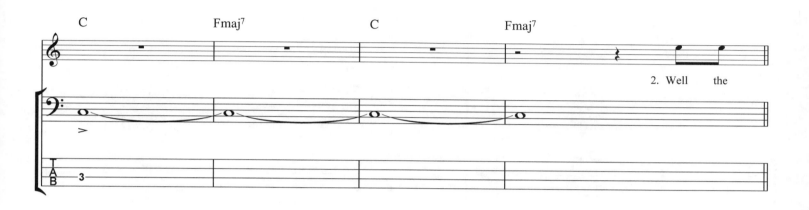

2. Well the

Verse

rain ex - plod - ed with a might -y crash as we fell in - to___ the sun. And the

first one said to the se - cond one there:_ "I hope you're hav - ing fun.___

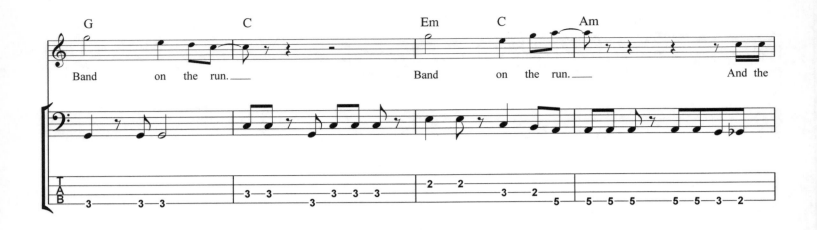

Band on the run.____ Band on the run.____ And the

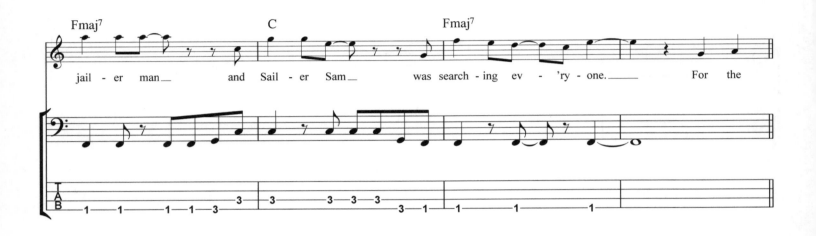

jail - er man__ and Sail - er Sam__ was search - ing ev - 'ry - one.____ For the

Chorus

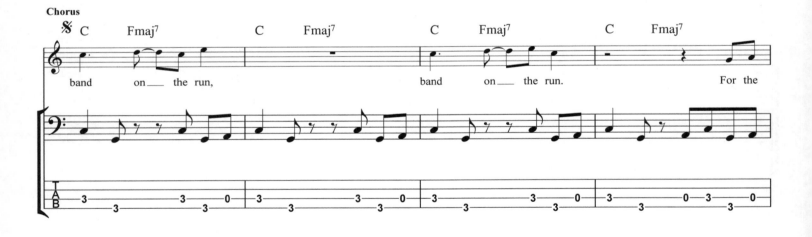

band on__ the run, band on__ the run. For the

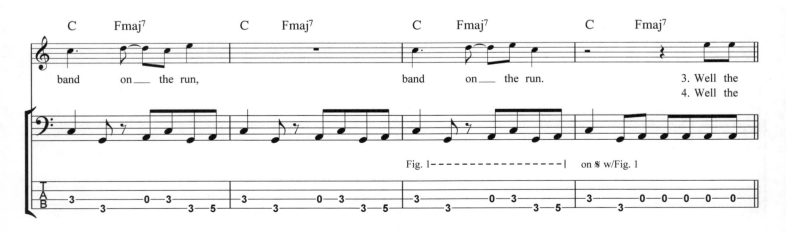

band on__ the run, band on__ the run.

3. Well the
4. Well the

Fig. 1- - - - - - - - - - - -| on 𝄌 w/Fig. 1

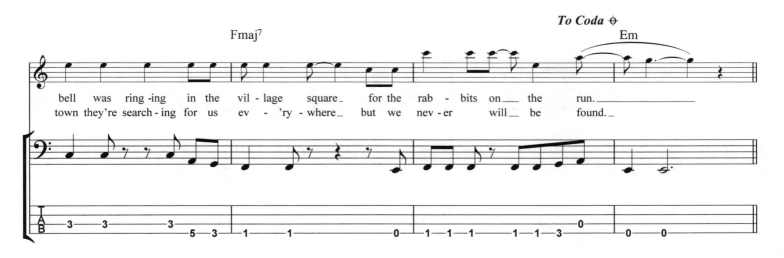

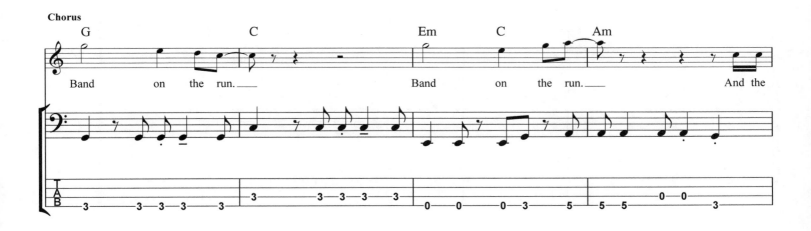

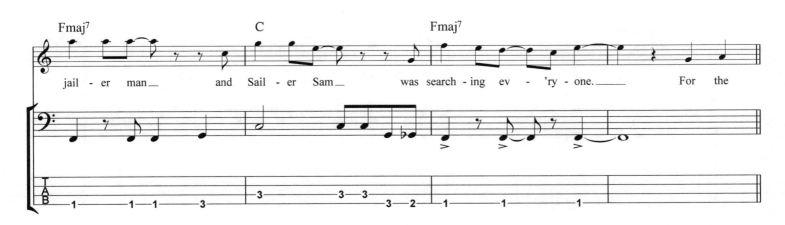

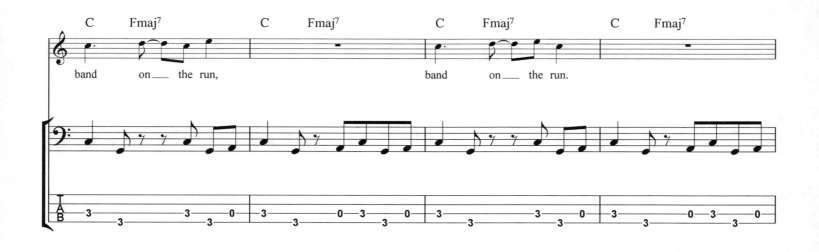

band ___ on ___ the run,   band ___ on ___ the run.

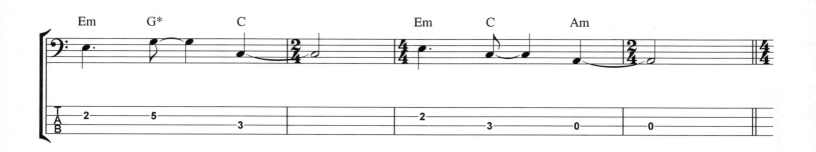

D.S. al Coda

Yeah, the

⊕ Coda

Band   on   the run, ___   band   on   the run. ___

And the coun - ty judge_____ held a grudge_____ who'll

search for ev - er more.___ For the band on___ the run, the

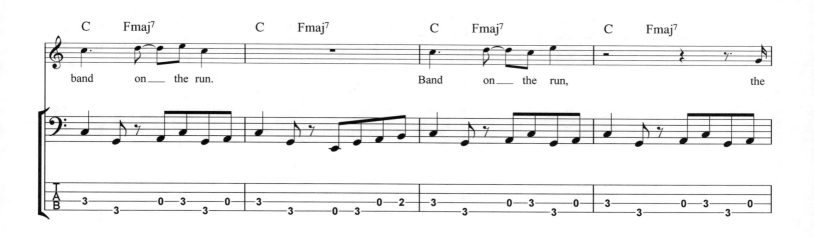

band on___ the run. Band on___ the run, the

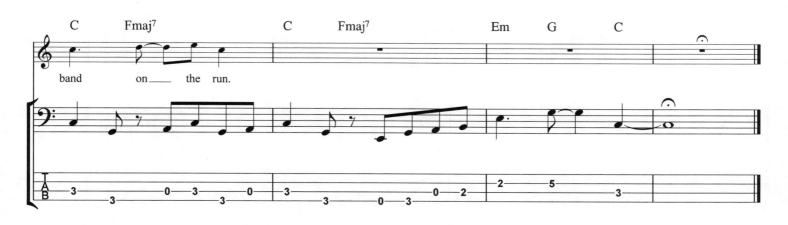

band on___ the run.

25

BEAUTIFUL NIGHT

Words & Music by Paul McCartney

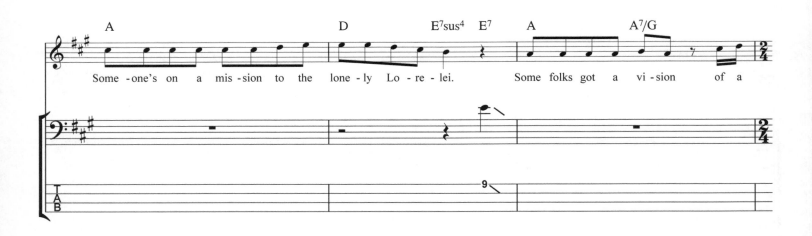

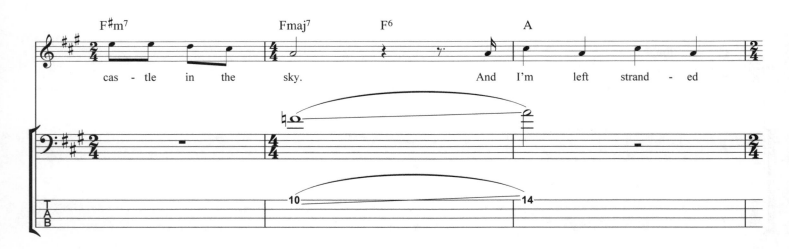

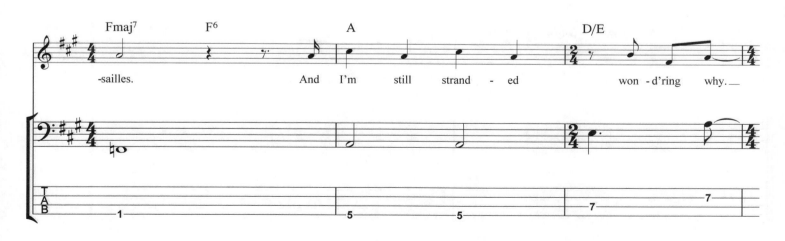

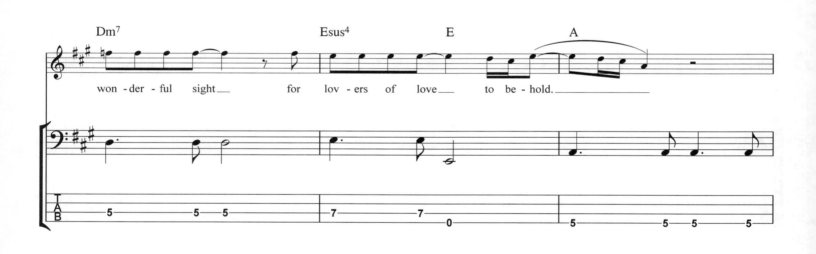

beau - ti - ful night___ for love,_____ a won - der - ful sight___ for

lov - ers of love___ to be - hold.___

Verse

2. Some boat's on the o - cean,___ we're here in this room,_ seems to me the per - fect way_ to

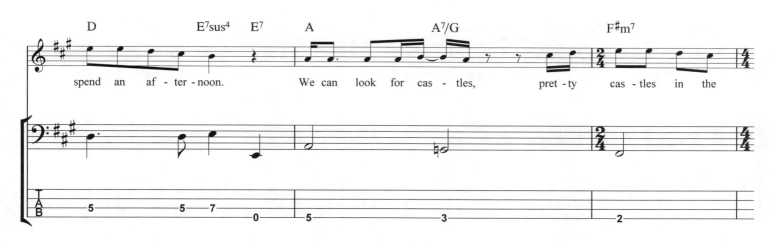

spend an af - ter - noon. We can look for cas - tles, pret -ty cas - tles in the

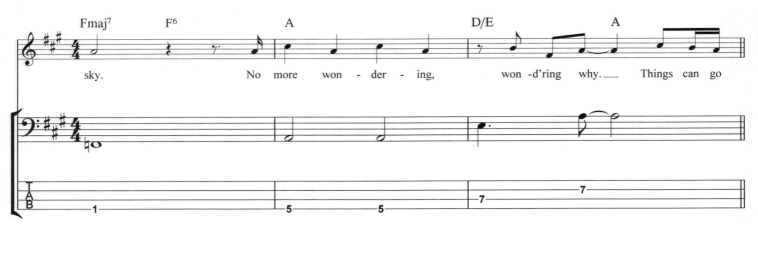

sky. No more won - der - ing, won -d'ring why. ___ Things can go

Bridge

wrong, things can go right, things can go bump in the dead of the

night. So let me be there, let __ me __ be there, let me be __

__ there with you ___ in the dead of the night. Make it a

JET

Words & Music by Paul McCartney & Linda McCartney

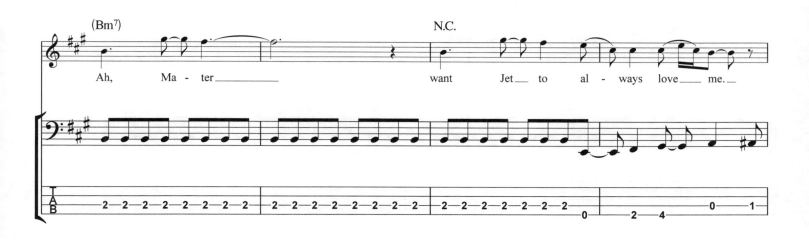

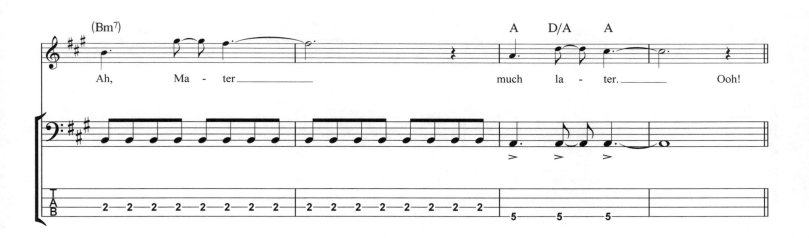

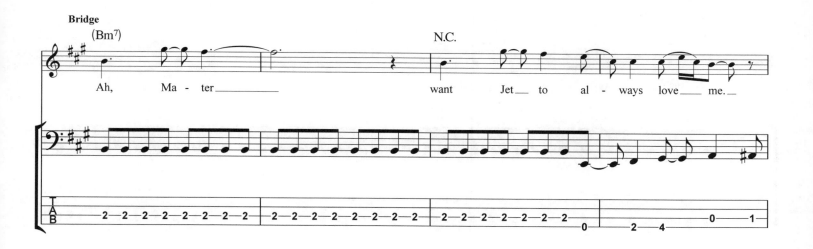

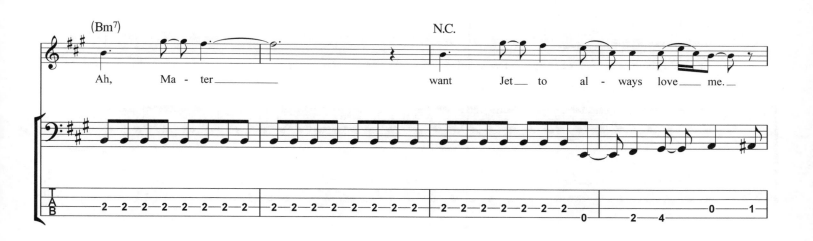

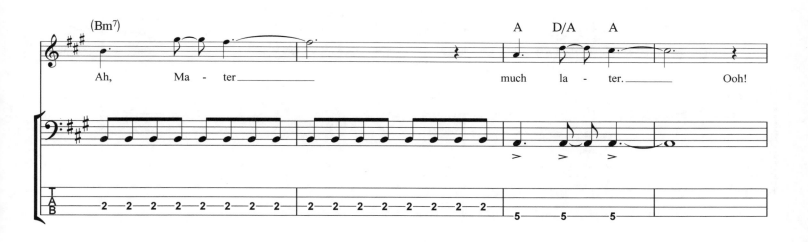

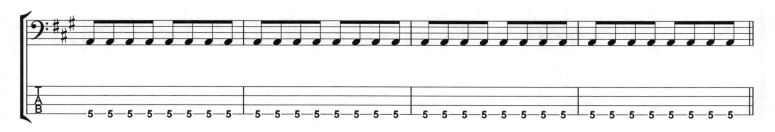

C#m

And Jet, d'you know I thought

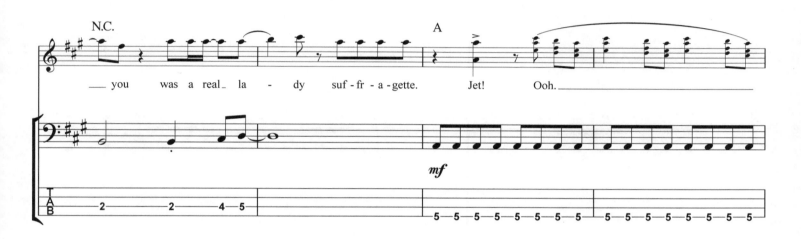

N.C.

you was a real la - dy suf - fr - a -gette. Jet! Ooh.

A

mf

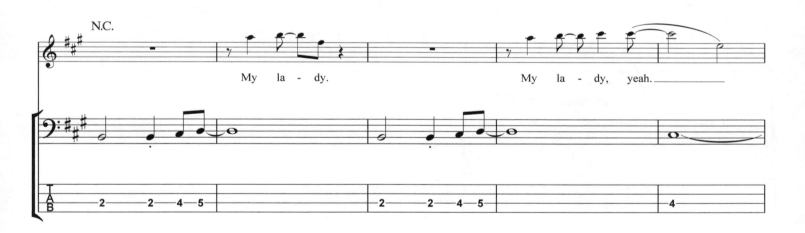

N.C.

My la - dy. My la - dy, yeah.

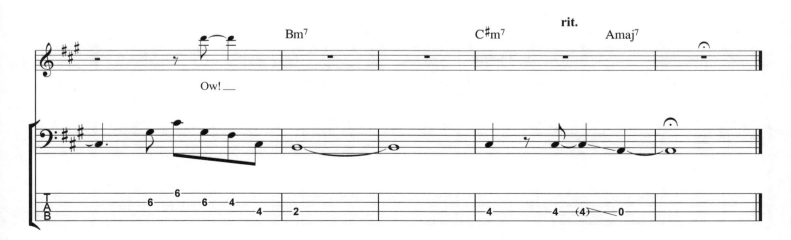

Bm⁷   C#m⁷   rit.   Amaj⁷

Ow!

MAYBE I'M AMAZED

Words & Music by Paul McCartney

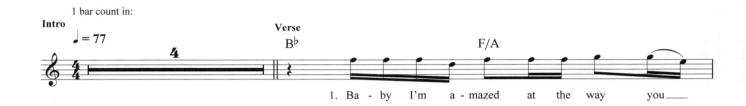

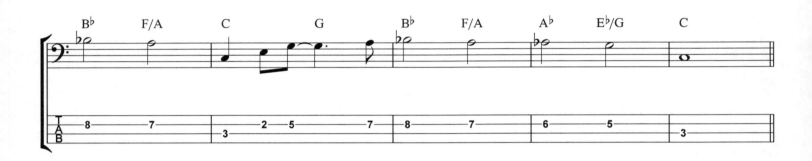

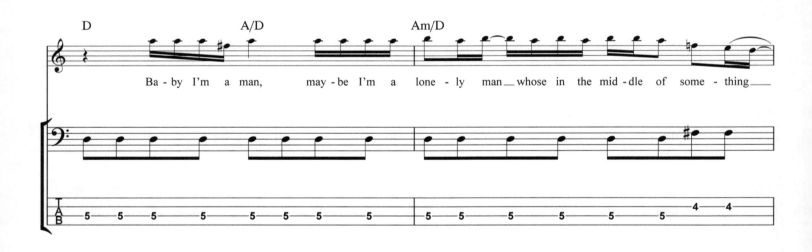

Ba - by I'm a man, may - be I'm a lone - ly man whose in the mid - dle of some - thing

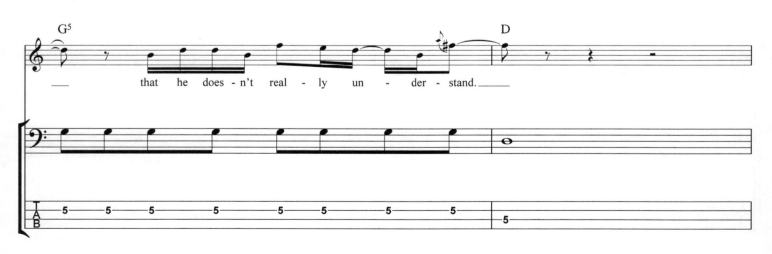

that he does - n't real - ly un - der - stand.

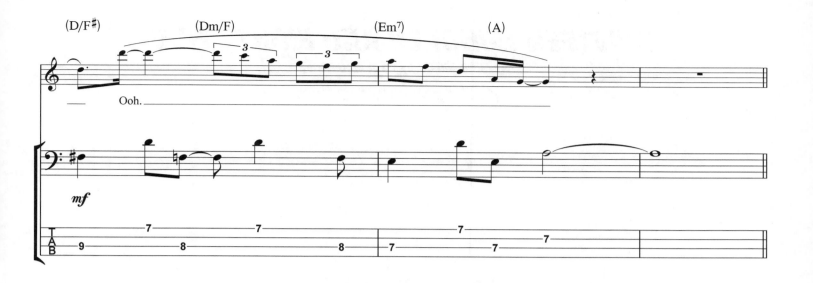

Gtr. Solo

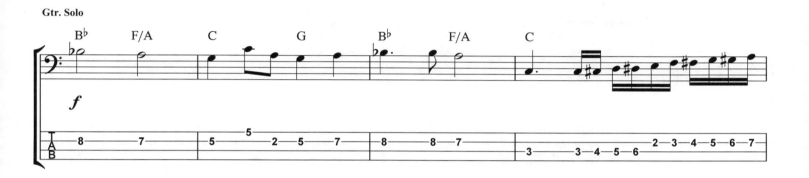

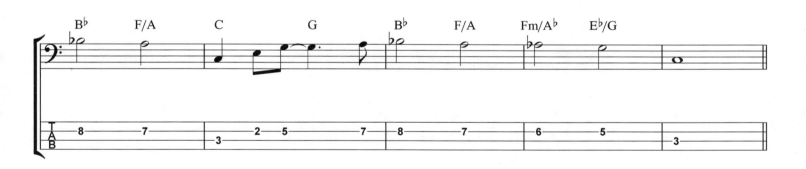

Repeat ad lib. to fade

Outro

NINETEEN HUNDRED AND EIGHTY FIVE

Words & Music by Paul McCartney

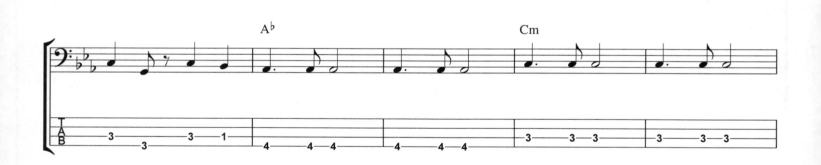

Verse

1. No one ev-er left a-live_ in nine-teen hund-red and eight-y five_ will ev—er_ do.

She may be right,_ she may be fine;_ she may get love_ but she won't get mine 'cause I_

_____ got_ you. Woh,_____ I._____

Oh,_____ I._____ Well, I

47

just can't get e-nough of that___ sweet stuff my lit-tle la-dy gets be-hind.___

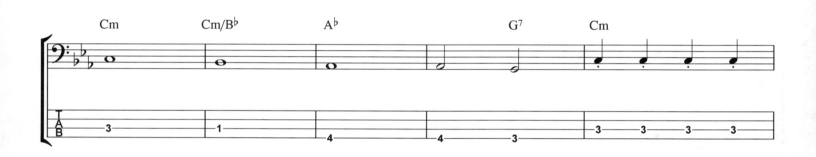

Cm   Cm/B♭   A♭   G⁷   Cm

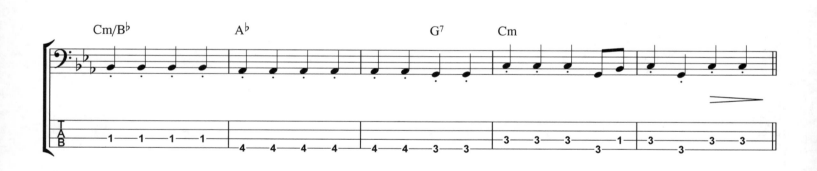

Cm/B♭   A♭   G⁷   Cm

Bridge   D♭m⁶   A♭

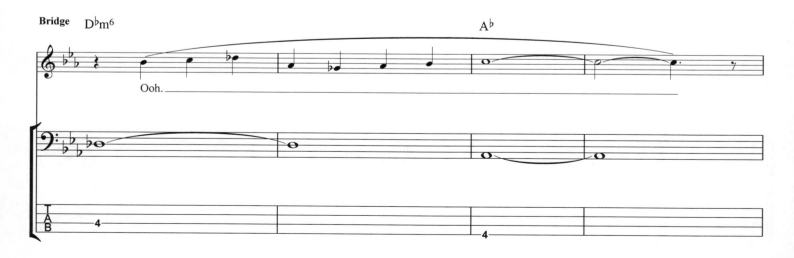

Ooh.___

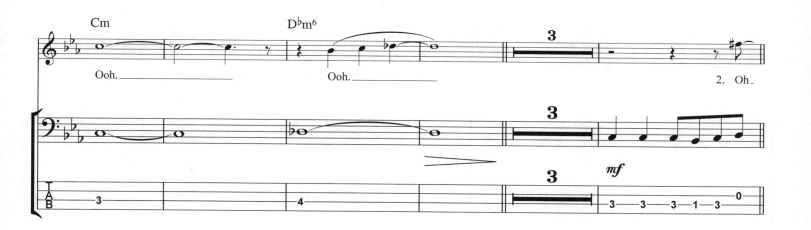

Oh,_____ I._____ Well, I just can't get e-nough of that___ sweet

stuff my lit-tle la - dy gets be-hind.___ Yeah!___

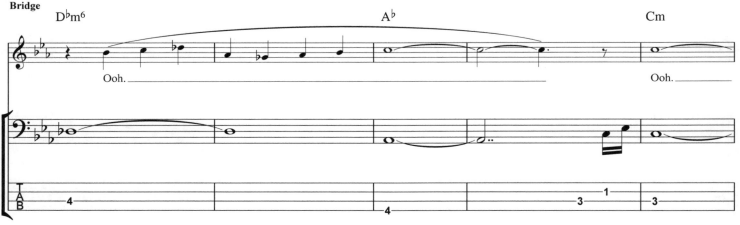

Bridge

Ooh._____ Ooh.___

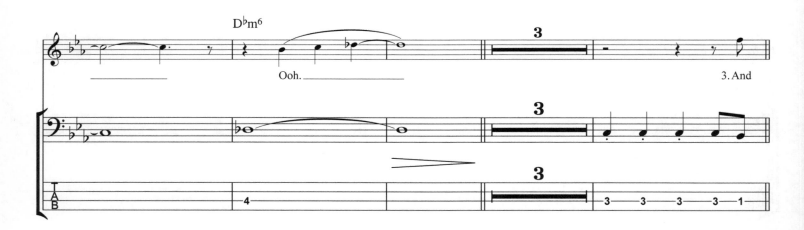

Ooh._____ 3. And

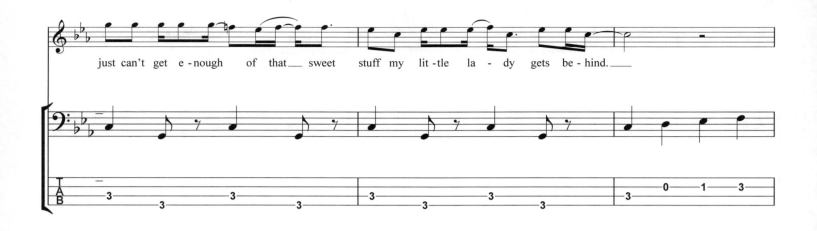

just can't get e-nough of that__ sweet stuff my lit-tle la - dy gets be-hind.__

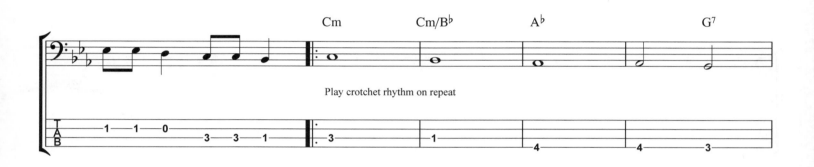

Play crotchet rhythm on repeat

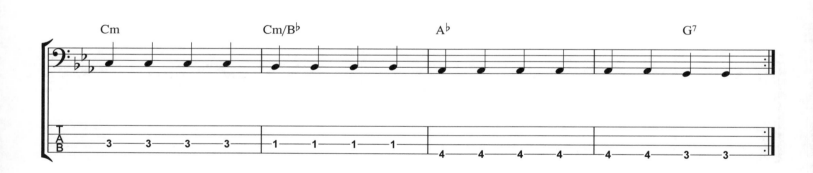

SILLY LOVE SONGS

Words & Music by Paul McCartney & Linda McCartney

Intro ♩ = 127   1 bar count in:

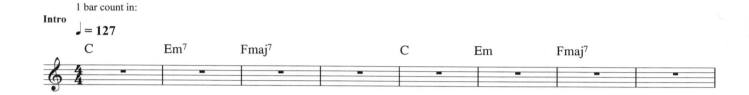

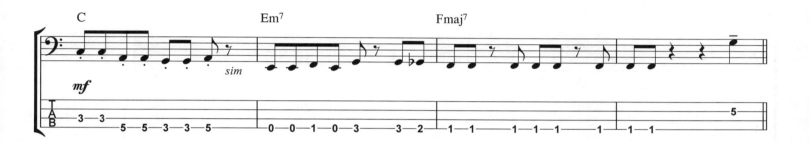

Verse

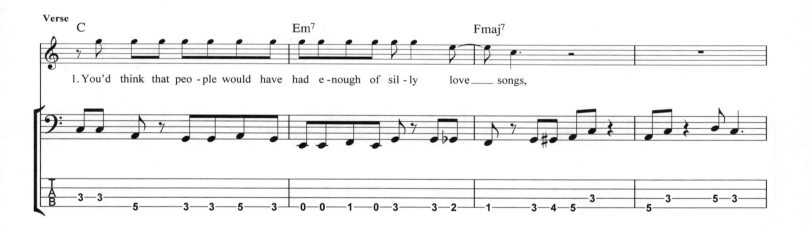

1. You'd think that peo-ple would have had e-nough of sil-ly love___ songs,

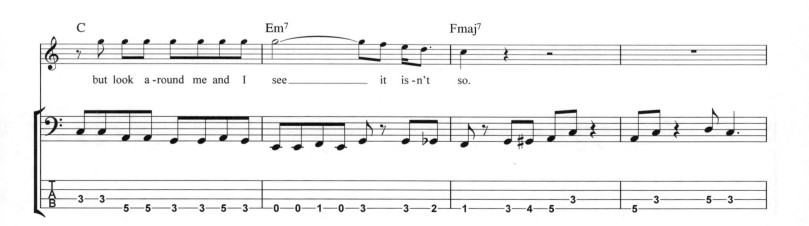

but look a-round me and I see_____ it is-n't so.

Bridge

Instrumental

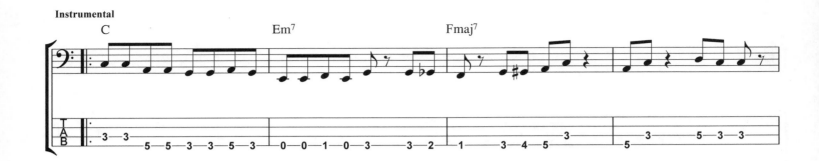

Bridge

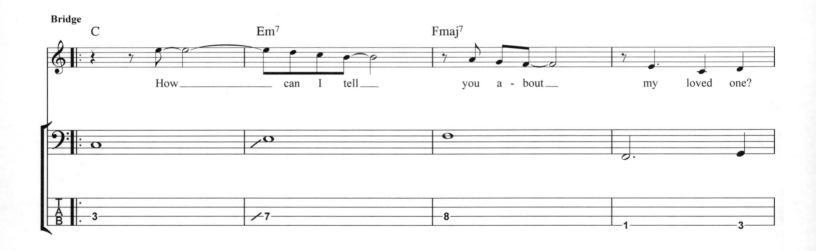

How_____ can I tell___ you a - bout___ my loved one?

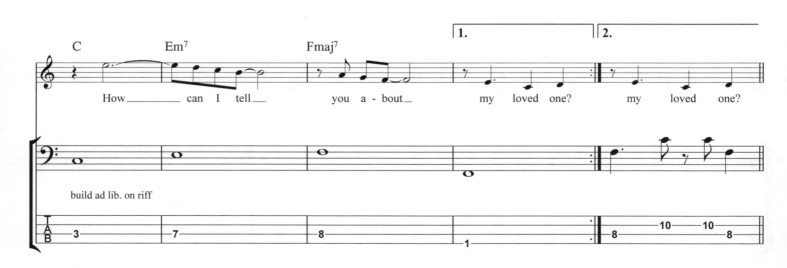

How_____ can I tell___ you a - bout___ my loved one? my loved one?

build ad lib. on riff

Instrumental

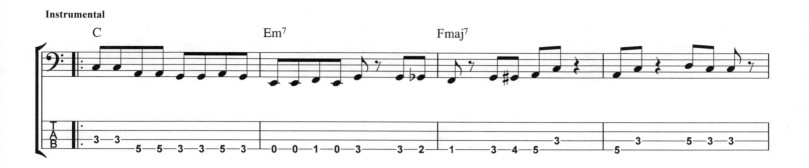

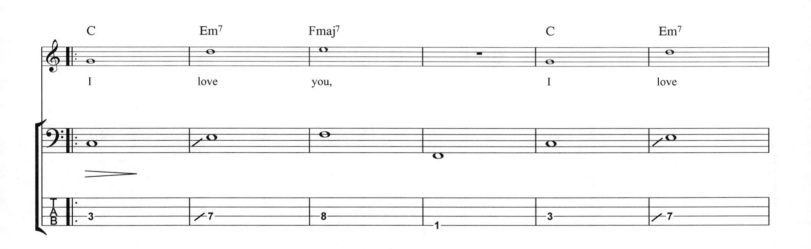

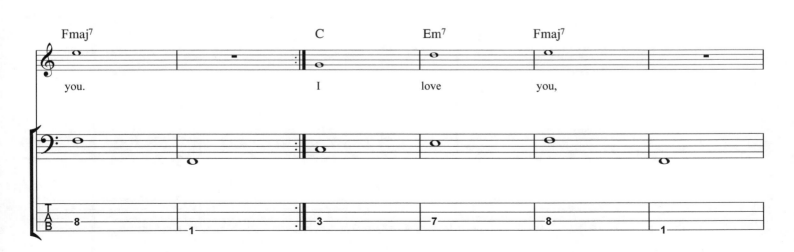

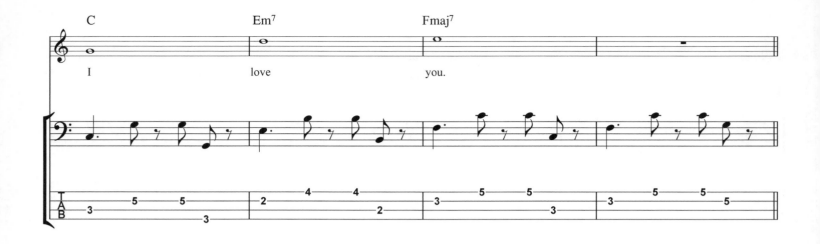

I love you.

Instrumental

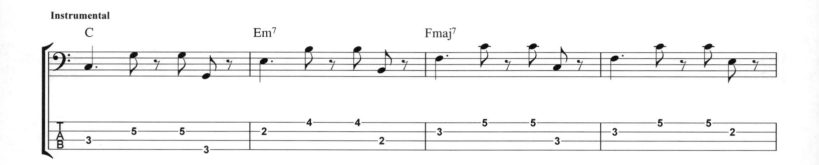

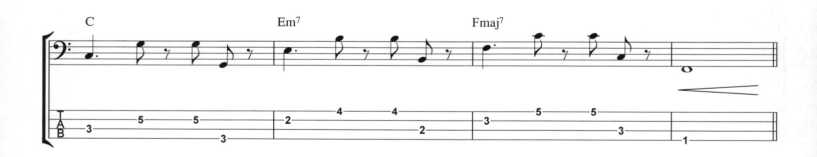

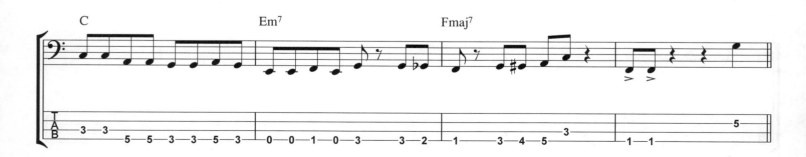

BASS GUITAR TABLATURE EXPLAINED

The four-line staff of bass tablature graphically represents the bass guitar fingerboard. By placing a number on the appropriate line, the string and fret of any note can be indicated. The number 0 represents an open string. For example:

3rd string, 3rd fret   **4th string, open**

SLIDE (not restruck): Strike the first note and then slide the same fret-hand finger up or down to the second note.

SLIDE (with restrike): Same as previous slide, except the second note is struck.

SLIDE: Slide up to the note indicated from a few notes below.

SLIDE: Strike the note indicated and slide up an indefinite number of frets.

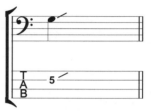

HAMMER-ON: Strike the first (lower) note with one finger, then sound the higher note (on the same string) with another finger by fretting it without picking.

PULL-OFF: Place both fingers on the notes to be sounded. Strike the first note and without picking, pull the finger off to sound the second lower note.

PALM-MUTE: The note is partially muted by the pick hand lightly touching the string(s) just before the bridge.

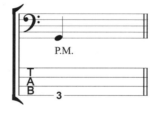

MUFFLED-STRINGS: A percussive sound is produced by laying the left hand across the string(s) without depressing it to the fretboard.

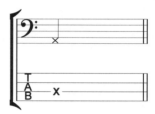

BEND (half step): Strike the note and bend up a semi-tone (halfstep).

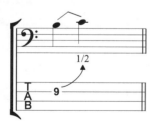

BEND & RELEASE: Strike the note and bend up as indicated, then release back to the original note.

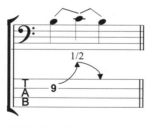

PRE-BEND: Bend the note as indicated then strike it.

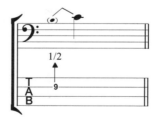

PRE-BEND & RELEASE: Bend the note as indicated. Strike it and release the note back to the original pitch.

TRILLS: Very rapidly alternate between the notes indicated by continuously hammering on and pulling off.

VIBRATO: The string is vibrated by rapidly bending and releasing the note with the fretting hand.

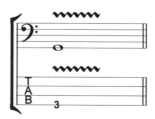

NATURAL HARMONIC: Strike the note while the fret-hand lightly touches the string directly over the fret indicated.

TREMOLO PICKING: The note is picked as rapidly and continuously as possible.

NOTE: The speed of any bend is indicated by the music notation and tempo.

Also available in the series

play BASS with...

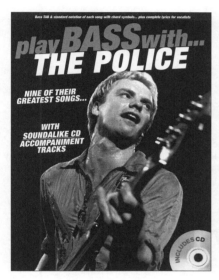
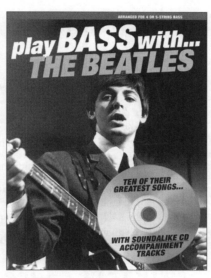

Play Bass With...
THE POLICE

Nine Great Tracks...
CAN'T STAND LOSING YOU
DON'T STAND SO CLOSE TO ME
EVERY BREATH YOU TAKE
EVERY LITTLE THING SHE DOES IS MAGIC
MESSAGE IN A BOTTLE
ROXANNE
SPIRITS IN THE MATERIAL WORLD
SYNCHRONICITY II
WALKING ON THE MOON
AM991309

Play Bass With...
THE BEATLES

Ten Great Titles...
A HARD DAY'S NIGHT
ALL MY LOVING
CAN'T BUY ME LOVE
EIGHT DAYS A WEEK
HELP!
I FEEL FINE
I SAW HER STANDING THERE
PLEASE PLEASE ME
SHE LOVES YOU
TICKET TO RIDE
NO90904

Play Bass With...
MUSE

Nine Great Rock Hits...
BLISS
HYPER MUSIC
HYSTERIA
MUSLE MUSEUM
NEW BORN
PLUG IN BABY
STOCKHOLM SYNDROME
SUNBURN
TIME IS RUNNING OUT
AM981354

Great songs with <u>Soundalike CD</u> accompaniment tracks

CD Track Listing

1. **TUNING NOTES**

**FULL INSTRUMENTAL PERFORMANCES
(WITH BASS)...**

2. **ANOTHER DAY**
(P. McCartney / L. McCartney) MPL Communications Limited.

3. **ANYWAY**
(P. McCartney) MPL Communications Limited.

4. **BAND ON THE RUN**
(P. McCartney / L. McCartney) MPL Communications Limited.

5. **BEAUTIFUL NIGHT**
(P. McCartney) MPL Communications Limited.

6. **JET**
(P. McCartney / L. McCartney) MPL Communications Limited.

7. **MAYBE I'M AMAZED**
(P. McCartney) Sony / ATV Music Publishing (UK) Limited.

8. **NINETEEN HUNDRED AND EIGHTY FIVE**
(P. McCartney) MPL Communications Limited.

9. **SILLY LOVE SONGS**
(P. McCartney / L. McCartney) MPL Communications Limited.

**BACKING TRACKS ONLY
(WITHOUT BASS)...**

10. **ANOTHER DAY**

11. **ANYWAY**

12. **BAND ON THE RUN**

13. **BEAUTIFUL NIGHT**

14. **JET**

15. **MAYBE I'M AMAZED**

16. **NINETEEN HUNDRED AND EIGHTY FIVE**

17. **SILLY LOVE SONGS**

To remove your CD from the plastic sleeve, lift the small lip on the side to break the perforated flap.
Replace the disc after use for convenient storage.